The Box Hill B
of
Orchids

Ann Sankey

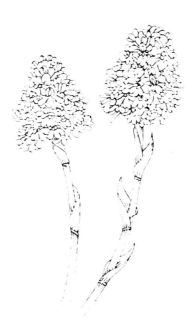

The Friends of Box Hill
2000

Dedicated to the memory of my late husband, John Sankey,
whose knowledge of Box Hill was unsurpassed and who passed his enthusiasm on to so many.

Acknowledgments:

I am extremely grateful to: Richard Bateman and David Streeter for their very valuable advice and comments on the text; Derek Turner Ettlinger for his advice and loan of photographs; Patricia Francis of Bolton Museum for information about their Lizard Orchid specimen; Peter Holland of the South London Botanical Institute, The Director and Jeff Wood of the Royal Botanic Garden at Kew, Roy Vicary of the Natural History Museum and The Holmesdale Natural History Club for help with access to their herbarium material; Jane Croft for information from The Historical Database of the Centre for Ecology and Hydrology; Paul Bartlett, Jean Combes, Derek Hill, Barry Phillips, Joyce Smith and other members of the Surrey Flora Committee for records of orchids on Box Hill; J R Leake, H S Scott, S Waite and J H Willems who sent me copies of research papers; Katherine Hearn, the National Trust Adviser on Nature Conservation, The National Trust Staff of Box Hill and Rosie Pite; John Bebbington and Robert Edmondson for the very generous loan of photographs; Andrew Tatham for drawing the map and preparing the colour plates; The Bantam Trust for a very generous donation to help with cost of production and to The Friends of Box Hill and The Box Hill National Trust Advisory Committee for their help and financial support.

My special thanks to Sandra Wedgwood for her support as editor, Elizabeth Worsley who drew the illustrations, Stephanie Randall for proof reading and to Sue Tatham for all her hard work in the design of the book and preparation for printing.

Photographs: John Bebbington, FRSP - Common Spotted-orchid on front cover, Musk Orchid on inside front cover, Fragrant Orchid flowers page 9, Bird's-nest Orchid and White Helleborine page 17, Autumn Lady's-tresses and Broad-leaved Helleborine page 18, Musk Orchid page 24, Greater Butterfly-orchid page 31, Lizard Orchid on inside back cover, Bee Orchid on back cover; **Ann Sankey** - Fragrant Orchid and Common Spotted-orchid flowers page 9, Pyramidal Orchids page 10, Violet Helleborine page 17, Frog Orchid page 23, Man Orchid page 24; **John Sankey** - Common Twayblade page 23, Marsh Helleborine on inside back cover; **Robert Edmondson** - Bee Orchid page 10; the remaining photographs are from the Box Hill NT archives.

Front cover: Common Spotted-orchid
Back cover: Bee Orchid flower showing self-pollination

Published by The Friends of Box Hill, Pixham Mill, Dorking, Surrey RH4 1PQ

ISBN 0 9534430 2 7

Printed in Beare Green, Dorking, Surrey UK by Mole Valley Press

CONTENTS

Introduction:
Box Hill and its
orchids

Why write a book about the orchids of Box Hill? The answer may be simple but the explanation is more complex. Orchids are perceived as special by very many people and Box Hill is also a very important place in the minds of its many visitors. Orchids are one of the most highly evolved of all flowering plants, some of them having such a complex and precise flower structure that they can only be pollinated by one species of insect. Orchids have a rarity value and we all like to see something that is rare. Orchids are often only associated with the tropics. At first glance our native orchids seem insignificant in comparison with their exotic cousins. They do have the same flower structure, but their beauty is more akin to a miniature than to a full-scale oil painting.

Using the orchids which grow on Box Hill as examples, the aim of this booklet is to describe some of the unusual characteristics of orchids and to show how other factors can influence their prosperity. It is not primarily an identification guide; several good ones are currently available and are listed under Further Reading. Recent and current research on orchids seems to be showing how much more there is to learn about this fascinating group of plants.

Box Hill has long been a favourite haunt for naturalists and there are botanical records which go back almost two centuries. The wild orchids which grow on it are one of the Hill's specialities and people still travel long distances to see them. Most days in June, there is at least one group of orchid-lovers searching the slopes. Some plants are easily seen by the casual stroller and much pleasure can be gained from these flowers.

The list of orchids found on Box Hill is impressive. The area is about 954 acres/386 hectares. How is it that so many different kinds are able to grow here? The answer partly lies in its soils, most of which are thin and alkaline, derived from the underlying chalk. The soils are low in nutrients, freely drained and warm, conditions in which a wide variety of plants are able to grow. Many orchids are confined to alkaline soils, but a few are found in the woodlands on the top of the Hill where the soils are more acidic. Box Hill has a varied topography, with sheltered valleys, cooler north-facing banks and hotter southern slopes, and some orchids are only found in certain of these areas. Another factor is the range of habitats which include chalk grassland, with both short and long sward, scrub of varying age and a variety of woodland habitats, including beech woods and hazel copses. The 'orchid season' on Box Hill is long and there is usually at least one species in flower from May to September.

Orchids associated with Box Hill

Orchids belong to the large family of Orchidaceae, with about 18,000 species worldwide. About 50 species occur in the British Isles; nearly half of these have been found on Box Hill. As well as its English name, each orchid has a scientific name: the genus and species to which it belongs. These are listed below together with the page numbers where the orchid is featured.

		Described on page	Photograph on page
Orchids growing in reasonable numbers:			
Autumn Lady's-tresses	*Spiranthes spiralis*	19	18
Bee Orchid	*Ophrys apifera*	8	10
Bird's-nest Orchid	*Neottia nidus-avis*	15	17
Broad-leaved Helleborine	*Epipactis helleborine*	21	18
Common Spotted-orchid	*Dactylorhiza fuchsii*	5	9
Common Twayblade	*Listera ovata*	27	23
Fragrant Orchid	*Gymnadenia conopsea*	6	9
Pyramidal Orchid	*Anacamptis pyramidalis*	11	10
White Helleborine	*Cephalanthera damasonium*	16	17
Nationally scarce orchids or those occurring in low numbers:			
Early-purple Orchid	*Orchis mascula*	35	32
Fly Orchid	*Ophrys insectifera*	34	31
Frog Orchid	*Dactylorhiza (Coeloglossum) viridis*	26	23
Greater Butterfly-orchid	*Platanthera chlorantha*	33	31
Green-winged Orchid	*Anacamptis (Orchis) morio*	35	32
Man Orchid	*Orchis (Aceras) anthropophora*	28	24
Musk Orchid	*Herminium monorchis*	29	24
Violet Helleborine	*Epipactis purpurata*	19	17
Recently extinct:			
Marsh Helleborine	*Epipactis palustris*	37	Inside back cover
Orchids recorded many years ago:			
Burnt Orchid	*Neotinea (Orchis) ustulata*	36	
Early Spider-orchid	*Ophrys sphegodes*	36	
Lizard Orchid	*Himantoglossum hircinum*	36	Inside back cover
Military Orchid	*Orchis militaris*	36	
Narrow-leaved Helleborine	*Cephalanthera longifolia*	36	

* Recent work comparing some of the DNA of European orchids has resulted in changes to the scientific name - the older genus is given in brackets.

The orchid flower

The structure of the flower forms the basis of the classification of flowering plants. The lily has large open flowers where the various structures are easily visible. One is used here to illustrate the basic parts of a flower. As with the tulip and buttercup, the lily has symmetrical flowers, like a bowl.

The orchid flower has the same basic structure, though some parts are reduced and it is symmetrical in only one plane, like a jug.

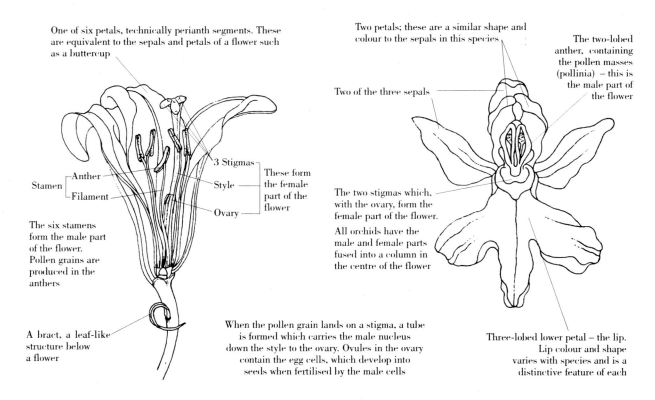

One of six petals, technically perianth segments. These are equivalent to the sepals and petals of a flower such as a buttercup

Stamen
Anther
Filament

3 Stigmas
Style
Ovary
These form the female part of the flower

The six stamens form the male part of the flower. Pollen grains are produced in the anthers

A bract, a leaf-like structure below a flower

When the pollen grain lands on a stigma, a tube is formed which carries the male nucleus down the style to the ovary. Ovules in the ovary contain the egg cells, which develop into seeds when fertilised by the male cells

Two petals; these are a similar shape and colour to the sepals in this species

The two-lobed anther, containing the pollen masses (pollinia) – this is the male part of the flower

Two of the three sepals

The two stigmas which, with the ovary, form the female part of the flower.

All orchids have the male and female parts fused into a column in the centre of the flower

Three-lobed lower petal – the lip. Lip colour and shape varies with species and is a distinctive feature of each

A lily flower
Three petals have been removed to show the inside of the flower

Common Spotted-orchid
Front view – not drawn to the same scale as the lily

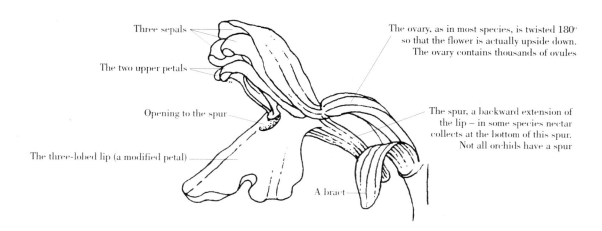

Three sepals

The two upper petals

Opening to the spur

The three-lobed lip (a modified petal)

The ovary, as in most species, is twisted 180° so that the flower is actually upside down. The ovary contains thousands of ovules

The spur, a backward extension of the lip – in some species nectar collects at the bottom of this spur. Not all orchids have a spur

A bract

Side-view of a Common Spotted-orchid

In this view the anther and stigmas are hidden by the sepals and petals

The **Common Spotted-orchid** can be distinguished by its leaves which have spots or blotches elongated laterally across the leaf. Early in the season, as the newly formed leaves are expanding, they look quite exotic with their vivid spots; later towards the end of the flowering season the spots fade and become almost invisible. Occasionally, plants without spotted leaves occur.

The flower heads must be amongst the loveliest of wild flowers, bearing many delicate pale pink flowers, borne on stems about 30 cm high. The lip is three-lobed, with a longer central lobe, and is marked with magenta loops of broken lines and additional spots. There is a lot of variation in background colour, from deep pink to white. The flowering season is long; the first flowers open at the end of May whereas in the cooler parts of the Hill flowers can still be seen in early July. It is a grassland species, quite tolerant of a range of soil types, and can also persist under scrub and in woodland clearings. This is one of the commonest orchids and can be found on many parts of the Hill.

All of the orchids growing on Box Hill have a broadly similar flower structure to the Common Spotted-orchid. They differ most obviously in the shape and relative size of the lip and spur.

Pollination: rewarders, deceivers and the self-sufficient

Pollination is the transfer of pollen from anther to stigma in flowering plants. It is an essential stage before fertilisation, which is fusion of a male nucleus from the pollen grain with the female nucleus inside the ovule. Only when fertilisation has occurred can the seed develop. There are two types of pollination: self-pollination involves the transfer of pollen from anther to stigma on the same plant; whereas in cross-pollination the pollen is transferred to the stigma of another plant of the same species. The former is more likely to ensure seed set but because the cells come from the same individual, it results in less genetic variation in the offspring than with cross-pollination. As Darwin showed, genetic variation is the basis of evolution and the ability to adapt to changing conditions. Cross-pollination involves agents, for example insects, to transfer the pollen. In many instances there has been a co-evolution of flower structure and insect pollinator, the shape of the flower having evolved so that only a few or even just one species of insect can fit into the flower and pick up pollen. The insect is attracted to the flower by scent and colour and the hope of finding food in the form of sugary nectar and/or protein-rich pollen. The complex shapes of orchid flowers are extreme examples of this co-evolution. Visiting insects usually transfer whole pollen masses, pollinia, from one flower to another, rather than carrying small amounts of separate pollen grains.

The mechanisms involved in orchid pollination were first detailed by Darwin and described in his book, *The Various Contrivances by which Orchids are Fertilised by Insects*, published in 1862. He lived at Downe, on the North Downs in Kent. Some of his observations were made nearby; his famous Orchid Bank still exists. Many of the same orchids grow on Box Hill.

The Fragrant Orchid can be called a 'rewarder' for it provides nectar for insects which visit the flowers and unwittingly transfer the pollinia from one flower to another. This is a lovely orchid which comes into flower in June, just after the Common Spotted-orchid. It has narrow, mid-green, unspotted leaves and the stem is flushed with purple, especially near the top. The narrow flower spike grows to 15-30 cm and is topped with bright pink flower buds. The sweet-smelling flowers are a uniform mauve pink with a noticeably long spur. This orchid is perhaps not as abundant on the Hill as formerly. It is one of the species which might have been lost from Mickleham Downs when it was ploughed during the War. It is also sensitive to encroachment by coarse grasses. Even so, in some years it can be seen in good numbers on other parts of the Hill.

Nectar collects at the end of the long spurs and only insects such as butterflies and moths with a long proboscis can reach the sugary liquid. The sweet fragrance which gives the plant its name helps attract these insects. The club-shaped pollinia are positioned so that their sticky bases, viscidia, form part of the roof to the opening of the spur.

When an insect such as a butterfly visits to obtain nectar, the viscidia become firmly fixed to its proboscis. Shortly afterwards, the stalks of pollinia bend forward, becoming parallel to the proboscis. In this position the pollinia are able to touch the stigmas of the next flower visited. If the flowers do not have spurs insects may not spend long enough on the flowers for them to pick up the pollen masses.

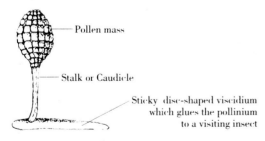

A pollinium
Much magnified

Interestingly, the Fragrant Orchid uses all the devices of colour, scent and nectar to attract insects. Yet the flowers are not often truly cross-pollinated, for as the insects move from flower to flower on the same spike, they transfer pollen to these flowers and less often to those of another plant. Pollination must be successful as a high proportion of the flowers of this orchid set seed. This can be observed by counting the number of ovaries which expand into mature fruits, called capsules.

The **Pyramidal Orchid** is perhaps a 'deceiver', for though its bright pink flowers look attractive to insects such as butterflies and day-flying moths, it tricks them into visiting but does not appear to reward them with any nectar. This orchid has been considered an enigma since Darwin's time. He noted that some individual insects would repeatedly visit the flowers of this species, but he could find no nectar in the spurs. The insects must be getting some reward, but what? We still do not know. The Common Spotted-orchid and Early-purple Orchid seem to

Change in position of pollinium following its attachment to the proboscis of an insect
(After Darwin)

be true deceivers for they do not produce nectar, but like many nectar-producing flowers they are brightly coloured and emit a scent, thus tricking insects into visiting their flowers. All these orchids have spurs and, as with the Fragrant Orchid, these structures may delay the insects sufficiently for them to pick up pollinia.

The flowers of the **Bee Orchid** never fail to fascinate. Not only are they pretty but their likeness to large bees is quite amazing. Each flower has pink sepals and a large velvety brown lip, patterned with yellow. It is this lip which resembles the abdomen of a bumblebee, the likeness is enhanced by the two narrow petals which stick out like antennae. There can be up to seven or more large flowers on vigorous plants, though three or four on a 25 cm stem is more normal. The rosette of grey-green leaves emerges in autumn. It has been shown that this species will only flower if its leaves have a sufficiently large surface area. Those too small wither in May. It used to be thought that Bee Orchids were monocarpic, that is, they died after flowering and setting seed, as some plants did not flower in consecutive years. Research has now shown that some Bee Orchid plants will pass one or two years without flowering, sometimes totally underground, before they flower again, a characteristic shared with some other orchids. Bee Orchids occur in small groups in grassland in many parts of Box Hill.

The Bee Orchid belongs to a large group of orchids, *Ophrys*, characterised by the resemblance of their flowers to the females of their own specific insect pollinators. This likeness is so close that some of the chemicals in their scent are exactly the same as those released by the female insects in order to attract males. This species thus practises double-deception, for not only do its flowers mimic female insects to attract males for pollination but no nectar is given to these visitors. Although the Bee Orchid may be cross-pollinated when it grows in warmer climates, in Britain it receives very few insect visitors and has evolved a method of self-sufficiency, or self-pollination. The stamens open widely to expose the pollinia which after a little time, hang down on longish stalks. This places them in front of the stigmas where a slight wind or other movement can cause the pollinia to touch the stigmas and so transfer pollen. Most Bee Orchid flowers develop capsules so this must be a successful method, as must be its seed dispersal and germination, for this orchid is often an early coloniser of recently disturbed ground, suggesting that it produces abundant seed.

Only a little information is published on the pollination of orchids on Box Hill; there is plenty of scope for individuals to make a valuable contribution to our knowledge of these plants. All one has to do is sit down, observe and record and pass the information on to the National Trust.

Fragrant Orchid

Common Spotted-orchid

Fragrant Orchid

9

Pyramidal Orchid with Skipper butterfly

Bee Orchid

Pyramidal Orchid

A year in the life of the Pyramidal Orchid

The Pyramidal Orchid is a distinctive plant with bright cerise, tightly clustered flowers forming a pyramid, or rather a cone, at the top of the stem, which is about 20 cm or more tall. Occasionally paler pink, or even white flower heads can be found. The peak flowering time is later than many of the other grassland orchids, extending well into July. Each flower is a more or less uniform colour except for the paler base of the lip, making a lighter 'eye' at the centre. There is a long spur tucked away alongside the ovary. Pollination is mainly by butterflies and day-flying moths and is usually successful as many capsules set seed. This process is described on page 7. The Pyramidal Orchid readily colonises new habitats. It is easy to spot anywhere in the grassland areas of Box Hill.

The Pyramidal Orchid is one of the wintergreen orchids which produce their leaves in autumn; all have underground tubers. Other tuberous species, such as the Common Spotted-orchid, and those with rhizomes, for example the Broad-leaved Helleborine, produce leaves mainly in early spring. Apart from these differences in timing, the annual cycles of other orchids are similar in many ways to those illustrated here. All orchids are perennial; those with tubers renew them annually whilst those with rhizomes grow by extensions of these underground stems.

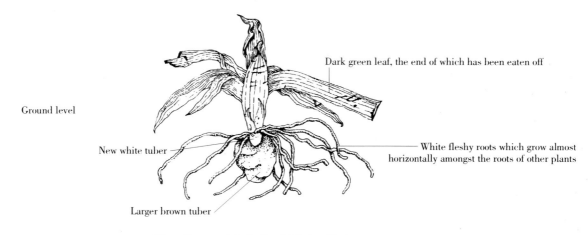

Ground level

Dark green leaf, the end of which has been eaten off

New white tuber

White fleshy roots which grow almost horizontally amongst the roots of other plants

Larger brown tuber

The Pyramidal Orchid in February
There is a rosette of dark green, partially folded leaves.
Underground the white fleshy roots are fully grown and a new tuber has started to grow

Changes in the growth of the Pyramidal Orchid over one season are shown by the following series of drawings, all of which were made from plants taken from the author's garden – not from the wild.

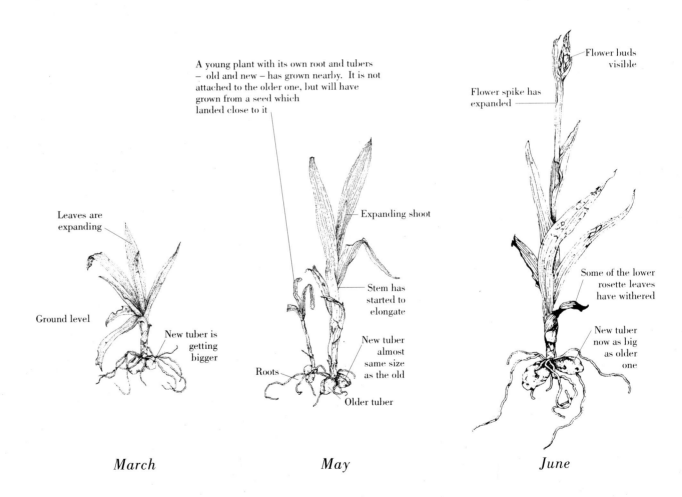

A young plant with its own root and tubers – old and new – has grown nearby. It is not attached to the older one, but will have grown from a seed which landed close to it

Leaves are expanding

Ground level

New tuber is getting bigger

Expanding shoot

Stem has started to elongate

New tuber almost same size as the old

Roots

Older tuber

Flower buds visible

Flower spike has expanded

Some of the lower rosette leaves have withered

New tuber now as big as older one

March

May

June

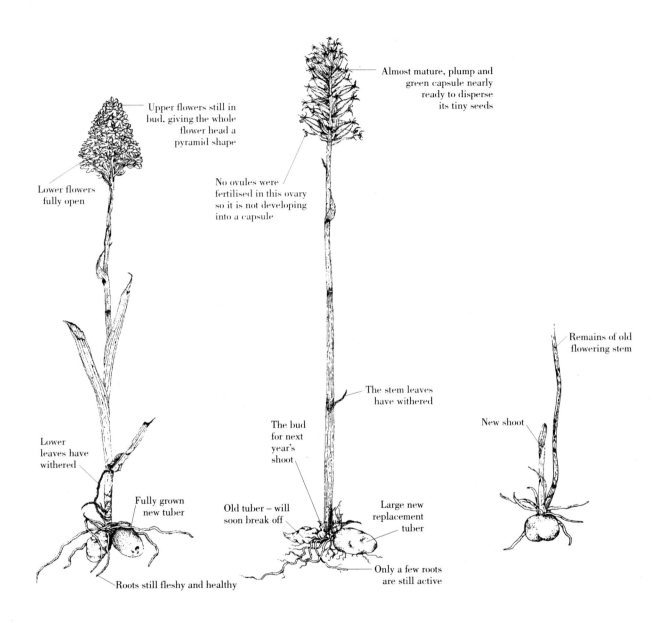

Upper flowers still in bud, giving the whole flower head a pyramid shape

Lower flowers fully open

Lower leaves have withered

Fully grown new tuber

Roots still fleshy and healthy

Early July

Almost mature, plump and green capsule nearly ready to disperse its tiny seeds

No ovules were fertilised in this ovary so it is not developing into a capsule

The stem leaves have withered

The bud for next year's shoot

Old tuber – will soon break off

Large new replacement tuber

Only a few roots are still active

Late August

Remains of old flowering stem

New shoot

October

13

Life underground: a close relationship

All orchids depend on the presence of a fungus, growing inside their cells, to provide them with food for at least part of their life. No orchid seed can develop without first becoming infected with a fungus and this dependency will continue until the first green leaves form, a process which may take one or more years. Once the plant is able to make its own food by using the chlorophyll in its leaves and light energy from the sun, a process called photosynthesis, it may become less dependent on its fungal partner. The degree of independence probably varies from species to species and during the life-cycle of each species. After flowering, some orchids may spend one or more years underground, and unless dormant, they must be dependent on the fungus during this time.

The association between a fungus and the roots of a plant is called a mycorrhiza. These associations are quite widespread in the plant kingdom. The advantage to the plant is an increased area for absorption, for the fine fungal threads, hyphae, grow through a larger volume of soil than plant roots, increasing the rate at which some nutrients are taken up. Orchids have their own special type of mycorrhiza in which the fungi which associate with them grow partly in soil and partly as coils inside the cells of the roots. Many of the fungi grow as saprophytes in soil, absorbing sugars and other soluble foods from the decaying organic matter. They use these nutrients as an energy source and as raw materials for making new hyphae, including those which invade the orchid roots.

This mycorrhizal association is not one of mutual benefit but rather seems to be one of controlled parasitism. The fungus invades the tissues of the orchid and then some of it is killed by the plant, which absorbs nutrients from the dead remains. The fungus itself appears to gain little benefit from the plant. Experiments with orchids growing in culture with a fungus have shown that sugars and phosphates are taken up by the fungus from the culture medium and are later found as components of orchid tissue. There is no such movement in the reverse direction. Thus orchid mycorrhiza represents a source of energy for the plant which may replace, supplement or alternate with energy gained by the plant from photosynthesis.

Only some of the fungi which associate with orchid seeds have been fully identified, despite research with orchids and fungi growing in artificial conditions in laboratories. These fungi belong to the group which form mushrooms and toadstools. A few of these fungi are parasites; how is it that orchids are not killed by these fungi? It seems that orchids produce compounds which control the growth of fungi within their tissues, though this is a matter of balance and in some circumstances, the fungi may become too virulent and kill the host cells. In orchid mycorrhiza there is probably a rhythmic swing between fungal growth within the plant tissues and digestion of the fungus by the plant. These changes could be affected by external influences such as temperature and moisture, acting on the plant and the fungus in the surrounding soil. There is much that we do not yet know about orchid mycorrhizas and their effect on the ecology of orchids.

One orchid which could not survive without its fungal partner is the **Bird's-nest Orchid**. This is a strange, dirty straw-coloured orchid usually found growing in deep shade. There may be fifty or more similarly coloured flowers on a stem which is usually about 25 cm tall. The bright yellow pollen masses show up well inside the flowers. It often occurs in groups and the previous year's spikes may still be visible. Thousands were recorded on the south-facing slopes above Headley Lane in 1947 and were described as a wonderful sight. In 2000, there were still well over 200 spikes on this hillside and this species occurs in a few other areas as well, often under beech but also under yew and birch.

Although it does occasionally become slightly green, this species is unable to make all the pigments necessary for photosynthesis. It has a short horizontal rhizome covered with a tangle of

The roots of a Birds-nest Orchid
This drawing is of a plant collected on Box Hill in 1905 and now preserved as a herbarium specimen at the South London Botanical Institute

short fleshy roots looking like a bird's nest, hence its name. Both roots and rhizome are always infected with a fungus. The flowering spike usually grows above ground in late May. Just occasionally the spike does not elongate but remains below ground. Even here self-pollination is possible and seeds may be formed, entirely underground. New plants are formed when the tips of the roots develop into new rhizomes.

The dependence on fungi for food enables this species to grow in woodland where there is little light but a plentiful supply of organic matter for the fungus. It is highly likely that this orchid illustrates a curious phenomenon known as a tripartite relationship in which tree roots are linked directly to the orchid by fungal threads. As mentioned above, many plants including trees have a mycorrhizal association with fungi. In some cases, the same fungus forms mycorrhizal associations with both tree and orchid roots; this is important to certain orchids. The process is illustrated in the diagram below.

It is possible that the helleborine orchids are also part of a similar tripartite relationship. The **White Helleborine** flowers in May and shows up well against the bare ground under beech trees, one place where it is most easily seen on Box Hill. Sometimes it can be found growing in grassland. The white flowers of this orchid seldom open wide so that they resemble narrow goblets. Sometimes they do not open at all. The broadish leaves are medium green and there may be 3-16 flowers on the stem which grows to 25 cm. Close inspection will show that the lip is marked with orange ridges, which seem to attract insects. In spite of this, the orchid is often self-pollinated.

Just occasionally, colonies of this orchid are found without any green chlorophyll. They must obtain their nutrients from another source, presumably from their fungal partner. The white helleborine is a mainly woodland species, giving further support to the suggestion that it forms a similar tripartite relationship as described above for the Bird's-nest Orchid.

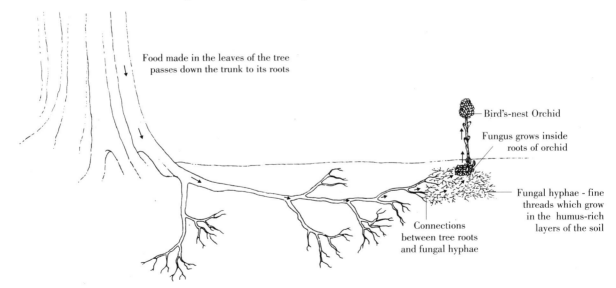

Food made in the leaves of the tree passes down the trunk to its roots

Bird's-nest Orchid

Fungus grows inside roots of orchid

Fungal hyphae - fine threads which grow in the humus-rich layers of the soil

Connections between tree roots and fungal hyphae

Possible tripartite connections between a tree, a fungus and the Bird's-nest Orchid
Arrows show how nutrients may flow from the tree to the fungal threads and then into the Bird's-nest Orchid

Bird's-nest Orchid

White Helleborine

Violet Helleborine

17

Autumn Lady's-tresses

Broad-leaved Helleborine

The same variable dependency on fungal associations may be the case with the Broad-leaved Helleborine and the much rarer shade-inhabiting **Violet Helleborine**. The whole shoot of this plant is flushed with violet, giving it a rather dull appearance. It emerges in June and grows quite rapidly with its tips bent over. Later the shoots become upright, reaching to 20-90 cm. The flowers are similar to the Broad-leaved Helleborine but the pale green sepals and petals are more pointed and wider spreading. It can also be distinguished by its habit of producing several spikes from one rootstock and by its smaller leaves. It also prefers the acid soils on the crests of the Hill. Violet Helleborines have been recorded on Box Hill as far back as 1815, but there are only a few plants found here now.

The orchids which grow out in the open are likely to be less dependent on a fungus for their food supply, their need for light suggesting their reliance on photosynthesis. One example is the **Autumn Lady's-tresses**. This tiny plant is the last orchid to flower, generally in the second half of August. Its name derives from the tight spiral arrangement of the flowers around the stem, like a braid or tress. The flower spike is often less than 10 cm high and is quite difficult to find with its grey stem and tiny white flowers. The sepals and petals face forward to form a tube, with a small lip. The exquisite sweetly scented flowers produce nectar and are always pollinated by insects. This orchid grows mainly in short turf.

Unusually, the flowering spike does not grow from a rosette of leaves. Instead it is produced directly from an underground bud; when the spike is fully grown, a small rosette of dark green leaves forms beside it. These leaves firstly make food for the developing seeds. Once these have been released, in October, the food is directed down to the new tubers. The leaves last through the winter, persisting until May or June.

Each plant has one or two underground tuberous roots. Unlike the Pyramidal Orchid, there are no horizontal roots above the tubers with which the plant can absorb water and become infected with a fungus. These functions and food storage are all performed by the tuberous roots. When newly formed in autumn, these roots grow vertically down. The fungus invades through the surface and colonizes the outer layers.

The Autumn Lady's-tresses is a sub-mediterranean species, which seems to prefer the warmer south-facing slopes of the Hill. It is adapted so that its leaves are active in the cooler months. This tiny orchid can withstand some shading by adjacent plants but it cannot tolerate heavy shading, as from some tall vigorous grasses which leave a thick matt of dead leaves over the rosettes in winter. Its need for short turf may also explain how this species can grow in some lawns on the chalk. On Box Hill, it has been known for many years in places where the sward is short.

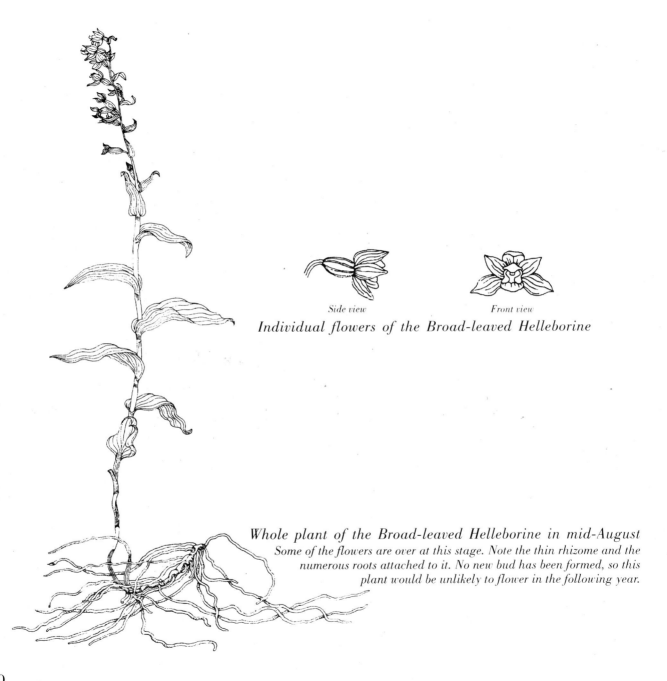

Side view　　　*Front view*

Individual flowers of the Broad-leaved Helleborine

Whole plant of the Broad-leaved Helleborine in mid-August
Some of the flowers are over at this stage. Note the thin rhizome and the
numerous roots attached to it. No new bud has been formed, so this
plant would be unlikely to flower in the following year.

Growing up: from seed to adult

The **Broad-leaved Helleborine** is one of the later flowering orchids, the flowers not appearing until late July or early August. In comparison with many of the other orchids, it has a rather dingy appearance but rewards close inspection. The leaves are a darkish green and quite broad with prominent veins. The flowering spike can grow to 40 cm or more with 10-60 flowers, often facing to one side. The sepals and petals open quite widely and are usually pale green flushed pink or purple. There is no spur but the base of the lip forms a cup in which nectar collects. Bacteria and fungi in this nectar can produce alcohol and visiting insects may become drunk. Perhaps this explains how they often become sluggish and more easily observed? It was also noted on Box Hill that quite suddenly, in the early evening, orange and black soldier beetles became particularly attracted to the flowers. Do the flowers change their scent at this time? If pollinating insects such as social wasps are scarce, the flowers may become self-pollinated, ensuring that many seed-producing capsules develop.

The Broad-leaved Helleborine is a woodland plant and seems to be particularly associated with beech and birch on Box Hill. It has a rather patchy distribution and can be found in quite young woodland. It may form a tripartite association with fungi and tree roots, as described on pages 15-16.

The seeds of most plants contain a perfectly formed miniature plant, the embryo, consisting of a root, stem and tiny leaves. There is a food store for the young plant, to provide it with nutrients until it has developed green leaves and is able to make its own. In this way it can always lead an independent life. The seeds of the Broad-leaved Helleborine and other orchids are very different; they are tiny, about 10 micrograms, and hence are described as 'dust seeds'. The embryo consists of just a few unspecialised cells. There are some fats and proteins as food reserves in the cells but no carbohydrates. There is a waterproof layer around the cells of the embryo and this is probably important in protecting it from desiccation. Outside this is the seed coat, varying in colour from sand to dark brown.

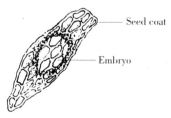

An orchid seed *Magnified* x 20

After dispersal and when conditions are suitable, the seed will absorb water. For most orchid seeds this will be in the autumn. They may remain like this for several months, commencing further development in the spring, or they may start to develop straight away. Having only a tiny food reserve, these seeds are not independent. The mycorrhizal association described earlier starts with germination. Some orchid species will not even start to germinate without the presence of a fungus, more specifically without the chemical stimulus provided by the fungus. Most seeds of the Broad-leaved Helleborine germinate within 9-12 months.

The embryo will grow into a structure found only in orchids, the protocorm. This does not have a root and only later develops a short underground stem and tiny leaves. Its surface is covered with hairs and it is mainly through these hairs that the protocorm becomes infected by the fungus, which provides food for the seedling orchid. Unlike most other plants, the seedling will remain underground for several months and, in many orchids, for several years.

Protocorm
with its many
hair-like rhizoids
Magnified x 5

The protocorm of the Broad-leaved Helleborine will gradually elongate into a rhizome. Roots will develop at intervals along this rhizome and it will gradually accumulate

enough food reserves for a leafy shoot to appear above ground, probably in the spring of the seedling's third year. Subsequently, shoots with larger leaves will be formed until the plant is big enough to flower. After this first flowering its reappearance, even as a leafy shoot, is unpredictable.

The growth and development of other orchids is similar, though the times taken can vary considerably and the seedlings of the tuberous species will form a tiny tuber rather than a rhizome. Evidence suggests that the tuber of the Bee Orchid will gradually increase in size and amount of stored nutrients in succeeding years until there is enough food available to produce a flowering shoot. This is probably the case with some of the other tuberous species, for example the Common Spotted-orchid and the Fragrant Orchid. Depending on the species, the time taken to emerge above ground as a leafy shoot and to reach flowering size may vary from one to perhaps five or more years.

A seedling Pyramidal Orchid
of unknown age, in early June
Note that even at this stage there are two
tubers: one from last year and one from this spring

22

Frog Orchid

Common Twayblade

23

Man Orchid

Musk Orchid

So many, so how so few?

Every characteristic of a species can in theory confer some advantage to it in the great struggle for existence that it has to endure. What is the advantage in producing seeds so small that they cannot grow without the aid of a fungus? It means that, instead of being independent as most seeds are, orchids have to rely on other organisms for their establishment. How can this be beneficial? It should be noted that there are many examples of interdependence between organisms. Our need to feed off other organisms rather than make our own food as plants do is just one example and the mycorrhizal association between orchid roots and fungi is another. It is probable that this relationship evolved first, then the dependency on fungi for seed germination. The advantage of having an outside source of food for the growing seed may be that it frees the parent plant from having to do so. This has enabled orchids to use their finite resources in making a far greater number of seeds than most other plants.

A Common Spotted-orchid plant may have 50 flowers. Even if only 10 capsules mature, this could result in the release of between 20,000 and 30,000 seeds from one plant. To make this vast number of seeds, at least the same number of ovules must be fertilised. So each flower will need a large number of pollen grains delivered to it.

Slit in capsule wall

Mature, dry capsule of a Common Spotted-orchid

Capsules may contain up to 3000 seeds which are released through longitudinal slits.

Whole fruiting spike of Common Spotted-orchid

This may explain the evolution of the pollen packets we call pollinia and the special way in which they are carried by pollinators.

Given these figures, it is tempting to ask why we are not overrun with orchids? Some do seem to have rather precise habitat requirements, including their associations with fungi and their ability to compete with other plants. There must also be enormous losses by many seeds not landing in a suitable place. So the release of a lot of seed should ensure that at least some lands in the right place. Even if the seeds do germinate, there will be more losses in the long interval between the growth of seedlings and their maturation as adult, seed-producing plants. This must be especially so when they are living for long periods as tiny protocorms in the soil and at the mercy of the huge army of small, soil-inhabiting herbivores and pathogens. The large number of seeds ensures that some of them do survive but inevitably, these are only a small proportion of those originally released.

Unfortunately, the amount of habitat suitable for orchids is diminishing and is becoming  fragmented. Few will grow in enriched grassland nor in commercial plantations. Box Hill is one of the remaining 'islands' of unimproved grassland in Surrey and woodlands are primarily managed conservation.

How long lived?

'How long do orchids live?' is a question which has no easy answer. Some species live for many years, others for only a few and for the rest we simply do not have enough information. Although Summerhayes in *Wild Orchids of Britain* (1968) mentions various times, it is only in the last 40 years or so that there has been long-term monitoring of populations of some species, confirming some of the earlier estimates.

The **Frog Orchid** is possibly one of the shortest-lived native orchids. It is a rare and inconspicuous orchid, about 10-15cm high, which emerges above ground in March and then produces its curiously coloured flowers in June. Perhaps it gets its name from the shape of the flower which, with a bit of imagination, looks like a leaping frog. The greenish flowers hardly show up against the grasses and other plants with which it grows. This orchid seems always to have been rare in Surrey. It was recorded on Box Hill in 1877 and then apparently not again until it was seen in 1958. It has since been found again and is possibly confined to one small area on Box Hill where a few plants flower in most years. Until we are sure of the stability of this population, visitors are asked not to go hunting for this orchid because it is vulnerable to trampling.

The underground phase of Frog Orchids is short, possibly lasting only one or two years.

There may then be no preliminary leafy stage as research has shown that flowering spikes can be formed in the plants' first year above ground. Only a small percentage flower in later years though there are records of occasional plants living up to seven years. For most Frog Orchid plants to be successful they must produce sufficient seed each year and enough of these must be able to grow into flowering and seeding plants to maintain the population. This species probably has rather exacting habitat requirements, both in the soil and above. The relatively small plants cannot withstand much shading nor perhaps competition from more vigorous vegetation. Frog Orchids are more often found in the north of Britain.

The **Common Twayblade** may be one of our longest lived orchids. It is easy to recognise with its two large green leaves, hence its name; just occasionally there is a third leaf. These leaves are carried off the ground on a short, robust stalk. A long slender 20-60 cm spike grows from this, bearing many small green flowers. The sepals and petals form a loose hood and the long folded-back lip is forked, so the flowers bear a slight resemblance to the Man Orchid. However the latter has a basal rosette of several leaves. The Twayblade flowers during mid-May to June and is found in both grassland and in amongst scrub or young woodland. This species is one of the most abundant of orchids on the Hill and unlike some other orchids rarely gets eaten when in flower. However few fruiting spikes are found. What happens to them?

No counts of the Common Twayblade have been made on Box Hill but 40-year-old plants have been recorded elsewhere and estimates are that it can live much longer. It has an underground rhizome similar to the Broad-leaved Helleborine. The plant can spread vegetatively and clumps of plants may be formed. This method of increase is much faster than by seed. Earlier estimates were that it may take 15 years from seed to flowering plant for this species. However, there have been no recent studies in the field to support or refute this figure. Although tolerant of some shade, if there is not enough light, the plants can exist in a non-flowering state for several years. If light levels later increase, the plants can flower again, so enabling this orchid to spread to new areas.

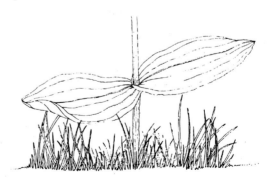

Leaves of the Common Twayblade

Nationally Scarce

Almost all of the 50 or so species of British orchids have declined in their range and 14 are listed in the Red Data Book of threatened plant species. None of these orchids occurs on Box Hill, though two, the Man and Musk Orchids, are on the list of 'Nationally Scarce Plants'. These are plants which from 1970 onwards have been found in only between 16-100 of the 10 km squares used for recording purposes in the British Isles.

The **Man Orchid** is a species of southeast England. It is a plant of calcareous soils, mainly found on chalk in this country. It has recently declined in numbers, particularly in East Anglia,

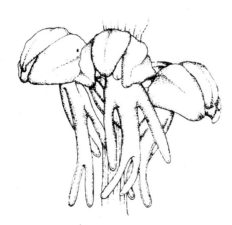

Flowers of the Man Orchid
Much magnified

the Chilterns and Sussex. Kent and Surrey are now its stronghold. This orchid gets its name from the shape of the individual flowers, which look like small men dangling by the napes of their necks from the stem. The sepals and petals come together to form a hood, the 'head' of the man. The lip has four lobes, two forming the 'arms' and two the 'legs'. There is a shallow depression at the base of this lip, possibly a primitive spur, in which nectar collects. The flowers are yellow, edged and streaked with dark red. The spike reaches 15-40 cm high in May to June; there can be up to 90 flowers, though 20-30 is more usual. It has a slight scent that is not especially pleasant. The Man Orchid is pollinated by a variety of small insects and seed set can be good.

This species has a mainly mediterranean distribution and its growth cycle is adapted to a climate of mild winter rain and summer drought. Its new shoot and roots start growing in autumn and the leaves emerge in December. The new rosettes are fully formed by January or February, so it is partly wintergreen, at least on Box Hill. Mild wet winters may also suit the fungal partner; the new roots being infected near their tips. In our cooler northern area, the orchid may be reliant on this fungus to fill the new tubers as they are fully grown by the time the plant flowers in late May. Once the flowers are over, the leaves yellow and wither and the plants become dormant when the seeds have ripened.

The Man Orchid is typically a grassland plant but it can grow in deciduous woodland and on scrub edges; this is consistent with its need for light in late winter and spring. This species seems to be diminishing on Box Hill. One reason for this may be the dense growth of grass in some places. One grass in particular, a coarse plant called Tor grass, *Brachypodium pinnatum,* has increased considerably. It dies down in winter, leaving a dense mat of dead leaves covering the ground. Light intensity at ground level decreases considerably wherever this grass grows well. The Man Orchid is considered to have some shade tolerance but it may just not be able to cope with being blanketed by this grass at critical times in its annual growing cycle. Also Tor grass produces dense rhizomes which may impinge on the roots of other plants and could affect the growth of the fungus. Man Orchids also seem to be a particular favourite of deer which eat the flowering spikes just when the flowers are fully out. Are they enjoying the sweet nectar?

The decline of the Man Orchid has to be described as 'apparent' for no one has yet systematically surveyed it on Box Hill. Regular monitoring is highly desirable because this is an important site for this species. It takes about five years for a germinated seedling to emerge above ground and produce its first green leaf. After that it needs to grow for possibly several years before it is large enough to flower. Then it may or may not flower the next year, a characteristic shared with some other orchids but there seems to be no pattern here. It may depend on variation in vigour between individual plants or on the habitat. The Man Orchid is moderately long lived, with individuals known to live for at least 14 years. It is also a relatively robust species and given the right conditions should prosper. It does produce adequate seed and can colonize new sites. We know little of the conditions needed for successful germination and establishment of the seedlings nor of the fungal partners.

The **Musk Orchid** produces a short flowering spike, 10 cm being the average height on Box Hill. It emerges above a rosette of two to three broad mid-green leaves. There may be 20-30 small pale yellow-green flowers on each stem. Because of their colour, they are not easily seen from a distance; definitely a plant where one needs to get one's eye in, preferably before putting one's boot on it. Five of the sepals and petals point forwards, making a short tube. The petals are long and narrow, forming projecting spikes. The lip has a long central lobe and two very short lateral lobes, with a depression at the base which contains nectar. Its scent, more like honey than musk, attracts a variety of small insects, including flies and parasitic wasps. Because of the shape of the flower these insects have to crawl in sideways, thereby picking up the pollinia which become firmly attached to their legs. Insect visits may be essential for pollination but the pollinators are not rare and seed set is usually good. The capsules ripen and the seeds are dispersed in late August.

The Musk Orchid has rather precise habitat requirements and never seems to have been widespread, either on Box Hill or elsewhere, though it may have been more abundant. Being small, it grows better in short turf. In addition it may not be as drought tolerant as some other orchids. Its leaves grow quite late in the season, from early May onwards, and remain green and active until late September. As flowering is most affected by climatic conditions the previous year, especially by drought, good flowering years will follow a summer that was cool and wet. If conditions for growth are good, the leaves will be larger and remain healthy for longer. More food can be stored in its underground tubers and the plants will have enough resources to develop flower buds. Drought and high summer temperatures will prevent full leaf expansion and the leaves die sooner, so reducing the food the plant can make. Under these conditions, with less food stored in its tubers, the plant may not be able to flower the following year. This dependence on moisture may explain how the plant grows most frequently on the moister slopes.

This orchid has two ways of increasing. As well as forming seeds, it can increase vegetatively. In good conditions it can make more than one tuber as, in addition to its replacement tuber, it produces daughter ones at the ends of slender rhizomes which may be up to 20 cm long. These daughter tubers can give rise to new plants the following year, though they will probably not flower until a few years later, when they too have built up enough resources. This perhaps explains the clumps of plants which are characteristic of this species.

The numbers of Musk Orchids may appear to fluctuate from year to year for they can survive one or two years underground and when not flowering are easily overlooked. They can be relatively long lived, plants of 27 years being recorded. This species' distribution in the warmer, drier southeast of the British Isles is interesting; in Europe, it grows in damper places than in Britain and on mountains up to 2000 m. It occurs throughout northern Europe and Asia, including north of Moscow and in Siberia.

There are many past records for the Musk Orchid on Box Hill. One herbarium sheet has a specimen 30 cm tall which was collected in 1879. This is much larger than the plants usually found now. There are also records from neighbouring areas such as Westhumble and Norbury Park. Sadly this species no longer grows in these places. It has also been lost from its former sites to the east and from the chalk slopes below Ranmore Common. This makes the Hill's long-established populations especially important.

Greater Butterfly-orchid

Fly Orchid

31

Green-winged Orchid

Early-purple Orchid

In the balance: too small a population size?

When there are very few plants of a particular species in one place, every one of those plants becomes important if the species is to survive there. For example, if there are ten plants and one of them is lost, this will have far greater consequences than if there were 100 or 1000 plants, for in the latter cases, there are still enough individuals for effective reproduction.

Plant populations are small for two main reasons: firstly, they may be only relatively recently established and secondly, the population may be long established but in decline. In the first case the plants may have come from one tiny seed which grew, flowered and produced seed from which all the other plants are ultimately descended. In this situation, there is likely to be little genetic variability. The future success of this new population may depend on the genetic make-up of the founder or 'mother' plant. Also important is the nearness of this population to others of the same species for genetic exchange. In the long term, most successful populations depend on new genetic input from time to time.

Long established populations, which were once healthy, may have shrunk due to habitat change. This often happens when other plants in the habitat are too vigorous. These plants grow at the expense of the less successful ones, whose numbers fall as a consequence. Most small orchid populations that disappear do so because the environmental factors that caused the decrease continue to act. Grassland turning to scrub and ultimately to woodland is such an extreme situation. Other changes are likely to be less obvious. For example the soil may have become enriched and this could have reduced the growth of the mycorrhizal fungi.

Several animals are known to eat orchids which can have an effect on their numbers. For example snails and slugs may devour entire spikes of flowers, thus preventing seed production for that year. The effect of severe slug damage to leaves is to reduce the food that the plant can make, so weakening it.

Reduction in numbers is likely to cause loss of genetic variation, as the loss will affect both beneficial and harmful genes randomly. So, small populations that have shrunk from much larger ones are also likely to have low genetic diversity. Though this may be important if the population is to expand again and move into new areas, it is notable that some successful orchid species do have very low genetic diversity.

The Greater Butterfly-orchid usually has two large shiny basal leaves and white flowers carried on a tall spike which can grow to 40 cm or more. Each individual flower perhaps resembles a butterfly as the two lateral sepals are spread out like wings. There is a long narrow green-tipped lip. The flowers are thought to be moth pollinated; the sweetly scented flowers have a nectar-secreting spur long enough to accommodate a moth's proboscis. Its flowering time is from late May onwards.

This species is usually found in open woodland and grassy woodland edges. It has never been frequent on Box Hill, having been recorded only occasionally. There is a record for 1960, but the present population came to notice in the 1970s when a few flowering plants were seen. The plants have since continued to flower in low numbers most years. There are also some non-flowering plants. This species is able to exist in a purely vegetative state for some years, especially when growing in quite deep shade. It is possible that the food obtained from fungal infection aids the nutrition of these plants, for there may not be sufficient light for the plants to make their own food. To enable this population of Greater Butterfly-orchids to thrive, it may be necessary to change the habitat subtly so that these plants can grow well enough to produce seed. There should be enough light, but not too much or else the plants may be swamped by vigorous grasses. Seedlings may produce their first green leaf in their second summer if conditions are good. A long tapering tuber develops in the third year. Thereafter the plants may gradually increase in size until they are able to flower. They may continue flowering for several years or go through one or two vegetative cycles before flowering again. The Greater Butterfly-orchid is perhaps relatively long lived. It has decreased in Surrey so it is important to conserve the Box Hill population.

The two to eight flowers of the **Fly Orchid** are widely spaced on a stem up to 30 cm. The Latin name of *O. insectifera* is very apt, for parts of the flower do indeed look like an insect, especially part of the lip which is velvety brown. Across the middle of this is a light blue iridescent band, resembling the folded wings of an insect. Two glistening, nectar-secreting spots at the base of the lip look like eyes and the illusion is further enhanced by the two narrow petals which stick out like antennae. Though called the Fly Orchid, solitary wasps seem to be the principal pollinators in this country. Even so, these are not frequent visitors and only about 10% of capsules set seed.

This orchid typically grows in woodland and is decreasing in the county. Like the previous species, it has not generally been considered a 'Box Hill orchid', having only been recorded perhaps once or twice in the past. The present population was discovered in the late 1980s after some woodland clearance. Even in flower the plants are inconspicuous and are liable to be trodden on. It is difficult to know how to help these plants for the habitat seems ideal. The Fly Orchid is wintergreen and shade tolerant but can also grow out in the open. Like the Greater Butterfly-orchid it needs to produce seed to spread. Unfortunately, this species seems to be prone to being eaten, perhaps by roe deer, rabbits, voles, woodmice or slugs and snails. Until more is known about this species' precise requirements, it can only be hoped that this population starts to increase again.

The **Early-purple Orchid** is perhaps the plant which Shakespeare called 'Long Purples'. The flowers are a deep reddish purple. The two lateral sepals are folded back and the large lip is three lobed, with a robust spur curving upwards behind the flower. In rich moist soils it can be a robust plant 40 cm or more tall, with a basal rosette of large, almost succulent, usually spotted leaves. On the chalk, the plants tend to be shorter with fewer flowers.

It is a plant with two distinct habitats in the southeast. Most commonly it grows in clay woodlands, flowering with bluebells, but it also occurs in chalk grassland. It is in this latter habitat that this orchid grows on Box Hill. In spite of the difference in size, it has recently been shown that the plants from these two habitats are not genetically different. They are therefore not separate sub-species. The Box Hill population is extremely small and several years can pass without a flower being seen. This is yet another orchid whose numbers have decreased in Surrey in recent years.

The **Green-winged Orchid** is a plant of damp meadows or similar neutral or slightly calcareous habitats. The alternative name of Green-veined Orchid is an apt one for it describes the characteristic feature of this orchid, the veins of the outer perianth segments are green and show up quite clearly against the deep pink or purple background colour. The lip is broad with three lobes and the spur points upwards behind the flower. The two side lobes are reflexed slightly and central one is usually paler with dark spots. The plant is relatively short, usually 6-15 cm, with 6-12 flowers. It is an early-flowering species, the flowers usually opening in May.

Once widespread, especially in the south of England, this orchid has suffered a drastic reduction in numbers due to the loss of old, untreated meadows. It is now considered a threatened species. There have been a few scattered records of this plant on Box Hill over the years. Some Green-winged Orchid plants can remain vegetative for some years but it is unlikely that this species still grows in all its former locations on the Hill. Two of the places where it was found are too well visited and another has become very overgrown. Orchid plants cannot withstand the trampling and soil compaction that a few parts of Box Hill receive from its many visitors. Nevertheless, it is hoped that with appropriate management, this orchid can become more firmly established on the Hill.

Those that were

Impressive as the list of Box Hill orchids is, it was once even longer. The rare **Early Spider-orchid** is recorded as growing 'in considerable abundance' on the north side of Box Hill in 1821. The **Military Orchid** was recorded twice in the 1830s and the **Burnt Orchid** a few years earlier on the south side of Box Hill. In 1838 Luxford recorded the **Narrow-leaved Helleborine**, an orchid similar to the White Helleborine but with narrower leaves, "at the east end of Sir Lucas Pepys' wood, between Headley Lane and Mickleham Downs". Sir Lucas Pepys lived at Juniper Hill and owned White Hill. These precise location details must have induced many to look for it and there are several herbarium specimens from this locality, all from the 19th century. Like all the above species it is now believed to be extinct on Box Hill.

The **Lizard Orchid**, that unmistakable orchid, has a tall flowering spike, 25-70 cm high, bearing many pale greeny-brown flowers, each with a long twisted lip which resembles the long tail of a lizard. There are three recorded sightings on Box Hill of this plant, which has its main distribution centre in southwestern France. The first record comes from a herbarium sheet, marked 'Herb. Smith, Box Hill, Surrey, 1814', now in the Bolton Museum. This sheet belonged to C O Groom and bears his characteristic stamp in pink ink of his alias 'Prince of Mantua and Monserrat'. The Lizard Orchid was found again in 1821. Then it was not recorded until 1927 when it was collected by G H Spare who worked in the herbarium at Kew.

This last reappearance of the Lizard Orchid on Box Hill coincides with an increase in the number of recorded populations and with a wider range in England during the late 1920s and early 1930s. There is speculation about the cause of this increase. It may possibly be a combination of favourable conditions for the production and dispersal of seed, together with the availability of suitable sites for the establishment of the seedlings. The plants are wintergreen; warm wet winters favour growth of mature plants so that they can develop flowers and produce seeds. It is not known how far these tiny seeds can be dispersed but they may have come from Kent, where there has been a large population for some time, or from France. The seeds could have been wind-blown or, as the seeds are sticky, they might have been carried by the considerable movement of people and equipment on both sides of the Channel during the First World War. It can take six years for a Lizard Orchid seedling to become large enough to flower. It may also take some time before the flowering plant is seen by an eagle-eyed botanist. This would fit in with its reappearance in 1927. Was there only one plant, now preserved as a herbarium specimen before it was able to seed, or were there more? We may never know.

In some parts of the country there has been an increase in the number of populations of the Lizard Orchid in the 1990s. If, as has been suggested, the climate becomes warmer, the number of sites where this species can be found may continue to increase and this orchid may once more grow on Box Hill.

One of the more unusual records is for the **Marsh Helleborine**. This is an attractive orchid, similar to the other helleborines in many ways though it can be distinguished by its white flushed pink petals and by its broad white lip with a frilly margin. The flowering period is late July. It is usually a plant of moist habitats, especially those with dissolved lime and is often found in wet hollows in sand dunes where fragmented sea shells provide the lime. There are a few other places on the chalk where it occurs, including Wiltshire and Bedfordshire. Chalk soils have some unusual properties, one of which is how much water they are able to hold and make available to plants. This is because chalk is a porous rock which can hold considerable amounts of water. The site where the Marsh Orchid grew is in a valley, where enough water must have been available. This orchid has an extensive system of shallow creeping rhizomes, from which 20 cm leafy shoots

arise. If it does not produce flowers in a particular year, the plant is likely to go unnoticed. This may account for the infrequency of its recorded appearance. Luxford, author of *A Flora of the neighbourhood of Reigate, Surrey* (1838) "has a specimen found on Box Hill by the late Mr Thomas Smith". Brewer (1856) did not find it. The next record, dated 1963, held by the Surrey Flora Committee is stamped 'CONFIDENTIAL'. Could a colony have survived this long without flowering? J E Lousley, author of *Flora of Surrey (1976)*, thought it had for he states "the rediscovery of this species on Box Hill after such a long interval is a good example of how easily a widely recognised plant may be overlooked on one of the most thoroughly botanised habitats in Britain". Even though the flowers are conspicuous, not many botanists would spend time looking in the grassland for the non-flowering shoots. Orchids with rhizomes seem to persist longer than those with tubers, so while it is extremely unlikely that the Lizard Orchid survived many decades unrecognised, it is possible that the Marsh Helleborine did. The alternative explanation is that a new colony developed from wind-blown seed. Flowers were seen in most years from 1963 to 1974. Unfortunately the two following years, 1975 and 1976, were memorable for both their extreme dryness and high temperatures. It has not been recorded since.

Life as an orchid on Box Hill

Being an orchid on Box Hill is rather a mixed blessing. On the one hand, the area is protected by a list of designations and is owned by the National Trust, an organisation which now looks after its properties very well, with conservation high on its list of priorities. Unlike many orchid sites, Box Hill is not a closed nature reserve with permits required for visits; it is freely open to the public at all times and there are many thousands of visitors each year. So, if one is an orchid plant growing in certain places on Box Hill, the chances of being sat on, trampled on by a heavy walking boot or a horse, burnt by the tyres of a speeding mountain bike, or compressed under the snow of some of the best toboggan runs in the country must be quite high. There is also the chance of being urinated on by a dog or having the ground fertilized by the ash from a cigarette. All of these events can seriously reduce the chances of being able to flower, or even survive. And if one does flower, one could be picked by the curious. If this were not enough, then one could be trampled on by one's admirers in their eagerness to see or even worse, photograph another orchid nearby. The large numbers of people visiting Box Hill just to see its orchids could also have an effect on their numbers.

So is there a future for orchids on Box Hill? The answer *must* be yes, even though the pressure from visitors will remain and probably increase as more and more people come to live in the southeast and have increased leisure time to spend walking. This damage from people is mainly accidental. Gone are the days of routinely collecting specimens and only the unscrupulous would now attempt to pick an orchid, or worse, dig one up.

On the positive side, the way in which the Hill is looked after is improving all the time, though resources are at times stretched to control the ever-decreasing amount of good quality chalk grassland. This is a man-made habitat, having developed over the centuries after the woodlands were cleared in pre-historic times. The grazing of sheep allowed the establishment of the downland turf with its rich mixture of fine grasses and other flowers, including many orchids. Chalk grassland is also a valuable habitat for many invertebrates. When sheep grazing declined, rabbit numbers increased and in part their grazing replaced that of sheep. After the myxomatosis outbreak in the 1950s, rabbit numbers fell dramatically and there was a consequent change in the vegetation. Without the restraint of grazing, coarse grasses and scrub developed. In places the scrub has been invaded by trees, creating young woodland. For example, parts of White Hill and the Ashurst Valley, now almost entirely woodland, were once open grassland.

Now the National Trust practises conservation grazing on the remaining grassland, using mainly sheep and cattle. The aim is to reduce the growth of the coarse grasses and to restrict scrub advancement. This will improve the habitat for a range of plants and animals, both common and rare, including Box Hill's many orchid species. The management is much more scientifically based and as more knowledge is gained, conservation can be focused on the specific requirements of individual species.

Monitoring is an important conservation tool. It has only been by counting every single orchid plant, flowering and non-flowering, in a defined square and noting its exact position every year for several years that any really accurate data have been obtained. As can be imagined, this is a very time-consuming process but it may be essential for those orchids with low population numbers and for the nationally scarce Musk and Man Orchids.

The ecologically generalist species such as the Common Spotted-orchid and Pyramidal Orchid, which can grow in a range of situations, should always grow well and continue on the Hill to be enjoyed for generations to come. Those with more specific habitat requirements may need more positive management. Even then, as conservation is still an inexact science, the future of some species may remain in the balance. Of course not all areas can be managed solely for their orchids. The sometimes conflicting interests of other rare plants and animals and of Box Hill's many human visitors also have to be considered. Fortunately there are many areas of grassland which have relatively few visitors and where orchids can be allowed to flourish.

A similar though smaller range of orchids can be found on the adjacent National Trust properties of Ranmore, Denbies Hillside and White Downs to the west and Reigate & Colley Hill to the east.

Education for all ages is now a major concern of the National Trust and of the Friends of Box Hill. A deeper knowledge of the Hill and all its facets brings great pleasure in itself and helps to protect it for future generations.

Author's note:

Although the distribution of the orchids on Box Hill is quite well known, the plants still have a habit of turning up in unexpected places. If you find an orchid in an unusual place, or in one which you think may be unrecorded, please inform the National Trust staff, preferably with a written note and ideally also with a sketch map of the site. In this way individuals can provide essential information for future management of the Hill.

Glossary: for terrestrial orchids

Anther – the part of the stamen which produces pollen; the male part of the flower.

Capsule – a dry fruit, which splits at maturity to release its many seeds.

Column – in orchids, the united style, stigma and stamens.

Embryo – the tiny, undeveloped plant within the seed.

Genus – a group of closely related species, the first half of an organism's scientific name.

Herbarium – a classified collection of dried and pressed plants.

Hyphae – the fine threads which make up the vegetative parts of fungi.

Lip – the third petal of an orchid flower which is often larger and a different shape from the other two.

Monocarpic – a plant which dies after flowering and fruiting once.

Mycorrhiza – an intimate association of a fungus and the roots of plants.

Nectar – a solution of sugars often secreted by plants to attract pollinators.

Ovary – part of the female flower containing the ovules and which develops into a fruit.

Ovules – a structure which contains the egg cell and which develops into a seed after fertilisation.

Perianth segments – the sepals and petals of a flower.

Photosynthesis – the process by which green plants make their own food, using their chlorophyll, light energy from the sun, water and carbon dioxide from the atmosphere.

Pollination – the transfer of pollen from the anther to the stigma; an essential stage before fertilisation.

Pollinium – a pollen mass, comprising all the pollen from one anther.

Proboscis – the long, tubular mouthpart of some insects, used for ingesting liquid food.

Protocorm – the structure formed from a germinating orchid seed, without roots and which becomes rapidly infected with a fungus.

Rhizoid – in orchids, a hair-like growth from the protocorm which functions as a root.

Rhizome – an underground stem, usually horizontal.

Saprophyte – a plant or fungus which obtains food from soluble decayed organic matter.

Species – a group of interbreeding individuals which do not normally breed with others; it forms the second part of the scientific name.

Spur – a tubular extension of the lip, sometimes holding nectar.

Stamen – one of the male parts of a flower, consisting of a stalk, the filament and the anther which contains pollen.

Style – part of the female section of a flower, connecting the stigma to the ovary.

Stigma – the part which receives pollen during pollination and is connected to the ovary by the style.

Tepals – term used for perianth segments when they cannot be separated into sepals and petals.

Tuber – a thick underground food-storage organ, derived from roots in the orchids cited in this booklet.

Viscidium – a sticky disc at the base of the stalk of a pollinium by which it becomes attached to an insect.

Wintergreen – herbaceous plants which produce their new leaves in the autumn.

Further Reading:

Allan B and Woods P. 1993. *Wild Orchids of Scotland*. HMSO

Brewer JA. 1856. *A New Flora of the neighbourhood of Reigate, Surrey*

Buttler KP. 1991. *Field Guide to Orchids of Britain and Europe*. Crowood

Darwin C. 1862. *Fertilisation of Orchids. The Various Contrivances by which Orchids are Fertilised by Insects.* John Murray

Davies P. Davies J and Huxley A. 1988. *Wild Orchids of Britain and Europe*. Hogarth

Delforge P. 1995. *Orchids of Britain and Europe.* Harper Collins

Lang D. 1989. *Orchids of Britain: a Field Guide.* Oxford University Press

Lousley JE. 1976. *Flora of Surrey.* David and Charles

Luxford G. 1838. *A Flora of the neighbourhood of Reigate, Surrey*

Proctor M, Yeo P and Lack A. 1996. *The Natural History of Pollination.* Harper Collins

Salmon CE. 1931. *Flora of Surrey.* Bell and Son

Summerhayes VS. 1968. *Wild Orchids of Britain.* Second Edition. Collins

Turner Ettlinger DM. 1997. *Notes on British and Irish Orchids.* Author's publication

Turner Ettlinger DM. 1998. *Illustrations of British and Irish Orchids.* Author's publication

Lack of space prevents the numerous scientific papers on orchid biology from being cited; for those wishing to take the subject further, a good starting point could be:

Rasmussen HN. 1995. *Terrestrial orchids – from seed to mycotrophic plant.* Cambridge University Press

Societies:

Botanical Society of the British Isles; The Hardy Orchid Society

The Orchid

The lovely and expensive *orchid* holds in its name the Greek word for 'testicle', *orchis*. Even Pliny the Elder, Roman author and naturalist, said, these 2000 years ago, that the *orchid* was remarkable in that, with its double roots, it resembles the testicles. These are his Latin words: "Mirabilis est *orchis* herba, sive serapias, gemina radice testiculis simili." The word *orchis* now survives in English only as a botanical and medical term. The meaning proper has disappeared along with the study of Greek from the general ken.

Wilfred Funk, *Word Origins and their Romantic Stories.* 1950

National Trust
BOX HILL
SURREY

DESIGNATIONS:

- Special Area of Conservation (SAC)
- Site of Special Scientific Interest (SSSI)
- Surrey Hills Area of Outstanding Natural Beauty (AONB)
- Metropolitan Green Belt
- Country Park

Legend:

- A roads
- Other roads
- Bridleways
- Footpaths
- Railways
- Grassland
- Woodland
- Viewpoint
- Car Park
- North Downs Way

N

| 0 | | 0.5 Km |
| 0 | | ¼ Mile |

To Leatherhead and London

Mickleham

To Nower Wood

Lodgebottom Road

To Headley

Cockshot Wood

To Headley Heath (NT)

Stane Street (Roman Road)

White Hill

Warren Farm

Mickleham Downs

Old London Road

Headley Lane

Juniper Hill

Juniper Hall (Field Centre)

Juniper Top

Juniper Bottom or Happy Valley

Ashurst Valley

Ashurst Rough

Flint Cottage

The Tower

Lodge Hill

Zig Zag Road

Flint Hill

River Mole

Burford Spur

Burford Bridge Hotel

The Whites

Box Hill and Westhumble Railway Station

Burford Lodge

To Box Hill Village and Headley

Box Hill Road

Fort

WC

Donkey Green

Oak Wood

To Betchworth Quarries 1mile

Dukes

To Ranmore 2miles

Footbridge

Stepping Stones

A24

Pixham Lane

To Reigate

A25

River Mole

To Guildford

Dorking Railway Station

Dorking (Deepdene) Railway Station

Dorking

42